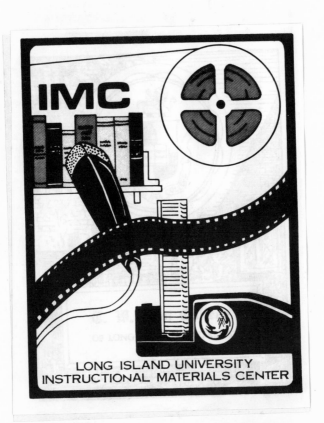

IMC

LONG ISLAND UNIVERSITY
INSTRUCTIONAL MATERIALS CENTER

RED TAG COMES BACK

by

FRED PHLEGER

A Science I CAN READ Book

pictures by ARNOLD LOBEL

HARPER & BROTHERS
Publishers New York

RED TAG
COMES BACK

It is morning.

The sun has just come up.

Aku has come to look

at the little fish.

7

These fish are salmon.

They will grow big someday.

Then they will be good to eat.

But Aku does not want

to eat the salmon.

They are such pretty little fish.

Aku just likes to look at them.

9

Aku sees a man catch the salmon.

He puts a tag on each fish.

And then he puts the fish back

in the water.

"Why do you tag the salmon?" asks Aku.

"I want to know more about salmon,"

the man says.

"I want to find out where they go,

and if they come back here

when they are old.

When men catch a fish with a tag

they will write me where they found it.

Then I will know."

The man shows Aku

how he tags the fish.

He puts a tag

on one little salmon for Aku.

"This red tag," says the man,

"will mean that it is your fish.

Then you will know her

if she comes back."

"I will call her Red Tag,"

says Aku.

"Someday Red Tag

will be a big salmon.

She will go far away.

"Then she will come back.

I know it.

I will watch for her."

13

And now the salmon are bigger.

It is time for them to go away.

They are going far away from home.

Red Tag is with the other fish.

The fast water helps them

go down the river.

Here they go down the river.

Nothing can stop the little salmon.

And nothing can stop Red Tag.

Here the water falls

and is very fast.

But over the falls the fish go.

And Red Tag is with them.

Many weeks have gone by.

Red Tag is a long,

long way from home.

Now she is with many,

many other fish.

They all go down the river, too.

And they eat as they go.

Red Tag eats and eats

as she goes down the river.

Look out for the birds!

The birds are after the little fish.

They want to eat them.

They may eat Red Tag.

This bird gets one

of the little fish.

But Red Tag gets away.

And just in time, too.

She swims away fast.

At last the salmon come to the sea.

They feel the salt water

and the waves.

They jump and jump.

Red Tag jumps, too.

Now they all know what to do.

They have not been here before.

But they know what to do.

They must eat!

They must eat and eat and eat!

There is more to eat

than Red Tag has ever seen.

And such good things, too.

She eats all she can hold.

And she can hold a lot.

When she eats a lot she will get big.

But look out, Red Tag!

Look out for that big fish!

It is after Red Tag.

Red Tag swims as fast as she can.

Can she get away?

She got away!

She just made it.

Red Tag is safe this time.

But she must always look out.

There are many big fish

in the water.

They want to eat little salmon.

Four years go by.

Red Tag is a big fish.

She is a very big salmon.

She eats all kinds of things.

She eats all the time.

And now she is big and strong.

Now she eats little fish too.

And then one day

Red Tag does not eat any more.

She starts back to the river.

The river she left so long ago.

She swims

day and night to get there.

She swims with other salmon.

They are all going back to the river.

Here is the big river again.

Red Tag and the other fish

jump out of the water.

They jump and jump

as they feel the river water again.

This is where Red Tag must go.

She must go far, far up the river.

She must go home to the little pool

where she was born.

That looks like something to eat.

Maybe a little fish.

It looks good, too.

Red Tag almost goes for it.

But no—

She does not want to eat now.

She has no time to eat.

She must go on up the river.

But what is this?

Why does Red Tag stop here?

She is caught!

She is caught in a net

with many other fish.

What can Red Tag do?

She must go on up the river.

But how can she get away?

41

She jumps!

She jumps as high as she can.

And out of the net she goes.

Back in the river.

Now she is free.

She can go on up the river.

After many days she comes

to a big wall.

The wall is all across the river.

Red Tag jumps again.

She jumps up high.

But the wall is too high.

How can she get over the wall?

She *must* get over the big wall.

Red Tag feels the fast water.

She jumps again.

She jumps high out of the water.

Other fish jump, too.

This is the way to get over

the big wall.

Men made it to help the salmon

get up the river.

Red Tag jumps and jumps.

Each jump brings her up a little more.

It is hard work to jump so much.

But Red Tag does not stop.

She must get over the big wall

and go up the river.

And at last she is over the wall.

She falls into the water.

It was hard work to jump so much.

She will rest in the water.

But not for long.

Soon she will go on—

ever up the river.

Red Tag swims on for a long time.

She does not eat—she does not sleep.

Now the river is small.

The water is very fast.

There is always danger.

This time a bear is hungry.

Look, he tries to get Red Tag.

But his sharp claws miss her.

On she goes—

Now the river is very little.

But the water is very fast.

Look out, Red Tag!

The Indians have long, sharp sticks.

They want to eat the salmon.

Red Tag jumps away

just in time.

She swims very fast.

There is not much time now.

She must get there soon.

She jumps the little falls.

Always on and on—

up into the high hills

as fast as she can go.

Now Red Tag is almost home.

Just above the falls

is where she was born.

She jumps.

But she falls back.

Can she jump the falls?

Again she jumps.

She jumps high this time.

Up and up she goes.

But she does not make it.

She falls back again.

And now one last big jump!

Up— and up—

Look at that jump!

Red Tag made it.

She is over the falls.

Red Tag is home at last.

She was a little fish here.

And now she is a big salmon.

She has come back to lay her eggs.

She will lay them in holes

in the bed of the river.

She makes the holes with her tail.

But see, here is Aku again.

He has come to fish in the river.

His little sister is with him.

Aku is happy to see Red Tag.

He tells his sister,

"See, there is my fish again.

When I was little, like you,

a man put a red tag

on that fish for me.

And now she is home again.

I will write the man.

"I will tell him that
Red Tag has come home
to have her babies."

Now Red Tag is very tired.

She is too tired to swim.

She is too tired to eat.

Aku and his sister watch as she rests.

She is old now, and her work is done.